Alex IV
THE MAN WITH THE GOLDEN HANDSHAKE

Alex IV

THE MAN WITH THE GOLDEN HANDSHAKE

PENGUIN BOOKS

PENGUIN BOOKS

Published by the Penguin Group
Penguin Books Ltd, 27 Wrights Lane, London W8 5TZ, England
Penguin Books USA Inc., 375 Hudson Street, New York, New York 10014, USA
Penguin Books Australia Ltd, Ringwood, Victoria, Australia
Penguin Books Canada Ltd, 10 Alcorn Avenue, Toronto, Ontario, Canada M4V 3B2
Penguin Books (NZ) Ltd, 182–190 Wairau Road, Auckland 10, New Zealand

Penguin Books Ltd, Registered Offices: Harmondsworth, Middlesex, England

These cartoon strips first appeared in the *Independent*
Published in Penguin Books 1991
10 9 8 7 6 5 4 3 2 1

Additional material by Mark Warren

The moral right of the authors has been asserted

Printed in England by Clays Ltd, St Ives plc

Other cartoon books by the same authors

Alex (Mandarin)
The Unabashed Alex (Penguin)
Alex II: Magnum Force (Penguin)
Alex III: Son of Alex (Penguin)

With Mark Warren
Celeb (Corgi)

Alex PEATTIE + TAYLOR

THAT CHINESE MEAL GAVE ME THE WORST ATTACK OF FOOD POISONING I'VE EVER HAD. I'M GOING TO REPORT IT TO THE HEALTH INSPECTOR

I SHOULDN'T BOTHER, CLIVE.

YOU KNOW IT'S VERY HARD FOR THEM TO DO ANYTHING UNLESS YOU CAN PINPOINT EXACTLY WHAT YOU'VE EATEN THAT UPSET YOU.

PLICK PLICK

AS FAR AS THEY'RE CONCERNED IT MIGHT HAVE BEEN INFECTED FOOD FROM ANY RESTAURANT YOU'VE VISITED IN THE LAST TWO DAYS.

YES?

BRRR BRRR

YOU'VE ONLY BEEN TO ONE.

ERK. THAT COULD HAVE BEEN EMBARRASSING.

SLAM

Alex PEATTIE + TAYLOR

YOU'RE NOT REALLY MEETING SIR ARCHIBALD IN THE HEALTH CLUB SAUNA?

PERFECTLY STANDARD PRACTICE, ALEX.

WHEN I NEED TO DISCUSS DIFFICULT BUSINESS WITH AN IMPORTANT CLIENT I FIND THE ENVIRONMENT MORE CONGENIAL.

IN A CONVERSATION IN THOSE SURROUNDINGS ONE IS PERMITTED CERTAIN LIBERTIES WHICH COULD NOT BE OVERLOOKED IN A MORE FORMAL CONTEXT.

UNCONTROLLABLE SWEATING AND BLUSHING, FOR EXAMPLE?

EXACTLY. IT'S QUITE ACCEPTABLE.

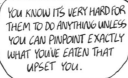

Alex
PEATTIE + TAYLOR

BEST TAKE CHRISTOPHER AWAY AS QUICKLY AS POSSIBLE, PENNY.

THANKFULLY HE'S TOO YOUNG TO REALLY TAKE THE SITUATION IN.

BUT THE PSYCHOLOGICAL RAMIFICATIONS OF AN EXPERIENCE LIKE THIS IN LATER YEARS ARE HARD TO CALCULATE.

HE MIGHT START WANTING TO BE A FIREMAN WHEN HE GROWS UP INSTEAD OF A BANKER.

FIREMAN SAM

Alex
PEATTIE + TAYLOR

AS A MONEY-
BROKER, ALEX,
THIS IS A NEW
EXPERIENCE
FOR ME.

OH, YOU'LL
LOVE IT, VINCE.
GLYNDEBOURNE
IS ALWAYS
A SPLENDID
OCCASION.

THIS YEAR WE'RE IN FOR
A MARVELLOUS MUSICAL
FEAST. DIE ZAUBERFLÖTE.

OH ER
RIGHT.

MAGIC FLUTE, VINCE.

THANKS ALEX.
I BOUGHT IT
ESPECIALLY.

Alex
PEATTIE + TAYLOR

THAT YOUR B.M.W OVER THERE, CLIVE?

THIS IS WHERE MY KEYRING WHICH AUTOMATICALLY FLASHES MY HEADLIGHTS COMES IN HANDY.

WITH THIS DEVICE I CAN SEE FROM A DISTANCE WHETHER TO CROSS OVER TO THE CAR OR NOT.

LOOK: I POINT IT IN THE VEHICLE'S DIRECTION AND PRESS THE BUTTON TO SEE IF THE HEAD-LIGHTS COME ON.

PEEP

BUT THEY DON'T.

NO.

PRESUMABLY BECAUSE YOUR CAR'S BATTERIES HAVE BEEN FLATTENED...?

EXACTLY. DUE TO THE INTRUDER ALARM GOING OFF IN THE MIDDLE OF THE NIGHT AGAIN, WAKING THE WHOLE NEIGHBOURHOOD... KEEP WALKING... I'LL HAVE SOMEONE PICK IT UP LATER WHEN NO-ONE'S LOOKING.

WE ARE FED UP WITH BEING KEPT AWAKE B...

Alex
PEATTIE + TAYLOR

BANG.

ONE CAN'T HELP HAVING AN INSTINCTIVE REGARD FOR AN ARISTOCRAT LIKE LORD MONCKTON.

THE FAULTLESS SENSE OF TASTE AND THE NATURAL UNDER-STATED FAMILIARITY WITH THE PURSUITS OF AN ENGLISH COUNTRY GENTLEMAN.

HUNTING, SHOOTING AND FISHING. YES.

I KNOW IT'S ALL AN ILLUSION PERPETRATED BY THE ENGLISH CLASS SYSTEM, BUT ONE NATURALLY MAKES POSITIVE ASSUMPTIONS ABOUT SOMEONE OF HIS APLOMB.

THAT HE MUST HAVE ATTENDED LOTS OF EXPENSIVE CORPORATE HOSPITALITY WEEKENDS?

EXACTLY. WHEREAS IN FACT HE PROBABLY HAD TO LEARN IT ALL OFF HIS DAD.

Alex PEATTIE + TAYLOR

I'VE BEEN TALKING TO MY PEN-FRIEND MISHA IN MOSCOW ABOUT THE FOOD SHORTAGES OUT THERE.

HE SAYS THE WHOLE SITUATION HAS GOT COMPLETELY OUT OF HAND. IT'S IMPOSSIBLE TO BUY PROVISIONS IN THE SHOPS WITH RUSSIAN CURRENCY.

AND APPARENTLY EVERYONE'S DESPERATELY TRYING TO GET A FEW BEETROOTS FOR THEIR LARDERS. IT'S MADNESS.

ACTUALLY THAT SOUNDS LIKE QUITE A GOOD SWOP TO ME. HAVE YOU EVER DRIVEN ONE OF THOSE THINGS?

Alex PEATTIE + TAYLOR

BUT OFFICER, THIS IS AN INTOLERABLE FORM OF NOISE POLLUTION AND SURELY A POLICE MATTER...

AS A LAW-ABIDING CITIZEN I HAVE A RIGHT TO COMPLAIN ABOUT AN INDIVIDUAL WHO INSISTS ON HAVING HIS PERSONAL RADIO ON AT FULL VOLUME...

...AND HOUR AFTER HOUR INCESSANTLY POUNDING OUT THE SAME BEAT...

..KTKSSSKSSS... SUSPECTED BREAK IN AT 27 MELROSE DRIVE...

..WELL CAN'T YOU ASK HIM TO PATROL ONE SOMEWHERE ELSE?...

Alex PEATTIE + TAYLOR

REALLY ALEX. WHAT A FAUX PAS. I'LL NEVER GO TO A PARTY WITH YOU AGAIN.

IT WAS A PERFECTLY NATURAL MISTAKE TO MAKE, PENNY. THOSE CATERING GIRLS ARE VERY UPMARKET. IT'S QUITE EASY TO GET THEM MIXED UP WITH ONE'S HOSTESS.

THAT'S NO EXCUSE.

LOOK, AS WE WERE LEAVING A GIRL HANDS ME MY COAT AND SAYS GOODBYE... I INSTINCTIVELY LEAN FORWARD AND GIVE HER A SMACKER...

I'M SO ASHAMED.

TIPPING THE HOSTESS A POUND. OH GOD.

I ADMIT IT WASN'T VERY MUCH.

Alex PEATTIE + TAYLOR

GOT YOUR FULL BODY WADER ON, CLIVE?

CERTAINLY HAVE.

IT'S LAUGHABLE HOW SOME OF THE CLIENTS HAVE COME UP HERE TO SCOTLAND SO ILL-PREPARED FOR SALMON FISHING.

QUITE. IT'S NOT LIKE SITTING ANGLING FOR PERCH ALL DAY FROM THE BANK.

I MEAN, IF YOU'RE GOING TO BE WADING CHEST-DEEP IN A RIVER YOU SHOULD SPEND SOME MONEY ON GETTING THE CORRECT EQUIPMENT.

LIKE SOME SERIOUSLY EXPENSIVE HEADGEAR.

EXACTLY. WHO'S GOING TO SEE ANYTHING ELSE?

A JOURNALIST ALWAYS CHECKS HIS SAUCE.

Alex PEATTIE + TAYLOR

GEE YOU WERE SACKED, CLIVE... THAT'S TOO BAD...

THEY'VE TAKEN AWAY YOUR CAR TOO, AND THE BANK MIGHT REPOSSESS YOUR HOUSE? YOU MUST BE REALLY CUT UP...

LOOK I JUST WANT TO LET YOU KNOW THAT NONE OF THIS AFFECTS OUR RELATIONSHIP.

IN FACT NOW THAT YOU'RE UNEMPLOYED, I INSIST EVEN MORE THAT IT MUST BE CONDUCTED IN TOTAL SECRECY.

Alex PEATTIE + TAYLOR

PLEASE, PENNY, KEEP YOUR VOICE DOWN... I DON'T WANT EVERYONE HERE TO KNOW I'M CURRENTLY UNEMPLOYED.

NOW LOOK, IT'S REALLY QUITE SIMPLE. WE'RE IN DESPERATE FINANCIAL STRAITS SO YOU MAY HAVE TO GO BACK TO TEMPING FOR A WHILE.

ARE YOU REALLY OBJECTING TO ME ASKING YOU TO BRUSH UP YOUR SHORTHAND SKILLS?

ONLY TO YOUR OBLIGING ME TO DO IT IN PUBLIC.

TAKE ANOTHER MEMO PLEASE, PENELOPE.

Alex PEATTIE + TAYLOR

LOOK, CHEER UP, CLIVE. IT'S NOT YOUR FAULT YOU'VE BEEN SACKED.

YES IT IS. I'M A TOTAL FAILURE.

OUTPLACEMENT COUNSELLING.

YOU'RE NOT A FAILURE. YOU MUST TRY TO BE POSITIVE. THIS IS RIDICULOUS...

I'LL NEVER FIND ANOTHER JOB. I'M PATHETIC.

LOOK, WE'VE BEEN HERE FOR AN HOUR.... THIS REALLY ISN'T GETTING ANYWHERE.

I KNOW.

MAYBE IF I CAME IN WITH MY GIRLFRIEND SHE'D BE ABLE TO GIVE ME SOME SUPPORT IN THIS..

THAT'S A GOOD IDEA.

CLIVE, YOU MUSTN'T LOOK AT THIS AS A FAILURE.

WHY NOT? HE'S A TOTAL SCREW-UP.

TOLD YOU.

POUND

Alex PEATTIE + TAYLOR

I'VE JUST HEARD... CLIVE FROM CORPORATE FINANCE HAS BEEN SACKED.

APPARENTLY IT'S BEEN COMMON KNOWLEDGE FOR DAYS. WHAT AN AWFUL THING TO HAPPEN. WHERE'S CLIVE'S NUMBER?

LEAF LEAF

AH HERE IT IS..

OH DEAR... TRUST ME TO BE SO NEGLIGENT. I EXPECT ALL HIS OTHER FRIENDS WILL HAVE PHONED ALREADY.

PLICK PLICK

HELLO... I HEAR YOU HAVE A VACANCY IN CORPORATE FINANCE...

YES. YOU'RE THE SIXTEENTH APPLICANT.

WARNING: THIS BUS IS PROTECTED BY SECURITY VIDEO CAMERAS.

Alex
PEATTIE + TAYLOR

WHAT'S CLIVE DOING?

I'VE GOT HIM TO MAKE A LIST OF ALL HIS CONTACTS AND PHONE THEM UP FOR A DRINK.

...RIGHT. OKAY THEN...

IT'S IMPORTANT TO GET IN THERE QUICKLY TO SOUND PEOPLE OUT ABOUT POSSIBLE JOB OPPORTUNITIES.

CLICK

SO, CLIVE, ... WHAT KIND OF RESPONSE ARE YOU GETTING?

AMAZING! IT CERTAINLY PROVES WHAT YOU SAID ABOUT HOW THE CITY WORKS ON INFORMAL CONTACTS AND WORD OF MOUTH...

IT'S ONLY FOUR DAYS SINCE I'VE BEEN SACKED AND ALREADY EVERYONE'S CLAIMING TO BE TOO BUSY TO SEE ME.

I TOLD YOU: NEWS TRAVELS FAST.

Alex PEATTIE + TAYLOR

THIS GRAPHOLOGICAL ANALYSIS IS ALL PART OF THE OUTPLACEMENT SERVICE, CLIVE.

YOU SEE, HANDWRITING CAN CHANGE ACCORDING TO HOW STRESSED THE INDIVIDUAL IS, THUS MAKING IT AN ACCURATE GUIDE TO HIS MEDICAL AND PSYCHOLOGICAL STATE.

IN YOUR CASE I CAN FORSEE SOME SERIOUS PROBLEMS. IN FACT I'M GOING TO HAVE TO REFER YOU TO A DOCTOR.

...WELL, THAT'S AN 'E'... NO, AN 'A' I THINK...

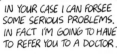

Alex PEATTIE + TAYLOR

NOW, CLIVE, TO THE SECOND STAGE OF YOUR GRAPHOLOGY ANALYSIS. WE'VE ALREADY ESTABLISHED THAT HANDWRITING REFLECTS HOW SOMEONE RESPONDS TO PRESSURE.

RIGHT.

SO... LET'S HAVE A LOOK AT YOUR LATEST SAMPLE. NOTE THE CAREFUL SPACING, THE CLEAR EVEN-HANDED LOOPS AND THE UNSTRESSED, CONFIDENT UPSTROKES...

NOW WHAT DOES ALL THIS SAY ABOUT THE PERSON DOING THE WRITING?

THAT SHE WASN'T EVEN REMOTELY INTIMIDATED BY MY DICTATION TECHNIQUE.

EXACTLY. YOUR MOTIVATIONAL POWERS ARE VIRTUALLY NON-EXISTENT.

Alex
PEATTIE + TAYLOR

CLIVE TOLD ME I'D FIND YOU IN HERE

LEAVE ME ALONE. IT'S MY LUNCH HOUR.

ALEX, MY JOB AS AN OUTPLACEMENT COUNSELLOR IS TO HELP YOU COME TO TERMS WITH YOUR UNEMPLOYMENT. DRINKING THIS STUFF IS NOT THE ANSWER.

IT HELPS ME FACE THE WORLD.

IT ALLOWS ME TO FEEL IN CONTROL.

STOP LIVING IN A FANTASY WORLD, ALEX. YOU KNOW WHAT THIS STUFF IS AND WHAT EFFECT YOUR DRINKING IT HAS.

YES. IT'S MINERAL WATER AND IT MAKES PEOPLE THINK I HAVE TO GO BACK TO WORK THIS AFTERNOON.

FOR GOD'S SAKE HAVE A PROPER DRINK. IT'S TIME YOU STARTED FACING REALITY.

Alex — PEATTIE + TAYLOR

Panel 1: PENNY, I'M AWARE THAT WE HAVE MASSIVE DEBTS BUT I DO NOT INTEND TO ALLOW THAT TO SPOIL MY LITTLE MOMENT OF PLEASURE.

Panel 2: AFTER ALL, IF I'M TAKING CLIVE AND BRIDGET OUT TO LUNCH I WANT TO GO SOMEWHERE WHERE I FEEL COMFORTABLE.

Panel 3: AND THIS IS ONE OF THE VERY FEW EATING ESTABLISHMENTS IN THE AREA WHERE I CAN MAKE USE OF MY GOLD CARD.

Panel 4: SORRY, LUV. CASH ONLY. — OH... SILLY ME... — ANYWHERE THEY ACTUALLY ACCEPTED CREDIT CARDS THEY'D CHOP IT UP.

Alex — PEATTIE + TAYLOR

Panel 1: ANSWER THAT WOULD YOU PENNY? — RING RING — ALEX! I DON'T MIND HELPING YOU OUT...

Panel 2: BUT PLEASE REMEMBER WHO I AM. I'M YOUR WIFE NOT YOUR SECRETARY. — RING...

Panel 3: FOR GOODNESS SAKE WE'VE BEEN MARRIED FOR ALMOST TWO YEARS NOW. — YOU DON'T NEED TO REMIND ME OF THAT, PENNY. — RING...

Panel 4: JUST SEND YOURSELF THE USUAL BUNCH OF FLOWERS WHEN THE TIME COMES. YOU SHOULD HAVE A NOTE OF THE ANNIVERSARY. — RING

Alex PEATTIE + TAYLOR

SO YOU DIDN'T GET THE JOB?

NO. THE INTERVIEW WAS AN UTTER NIGHTMARE.

THE INTERVIEWER WAS RUDE AND AGGRESSIVE THROUGHOUT. HE JUST BELITTLED ALL MY QUALIFICATIONS AND POURED SCORN ON EVERYTHING I SAID.

HE WAS JUST TRYING TO GAUGE YOUR REACTIONS UNDER STRESS, CLIVE.

IT'S A USEFUL TESTING OF YOUR ABILITY TO COPE WITH THE INEVITABLE STRAIN AND PRESSURE YOU WILL HAVE TO FACE.

WHAT? YOU DIDN'T GET THE JOB? YOU TOTAL CRETIN...YOU COULDN'T EVEN GET EMPLOYMENT SWEEPING THE STREETS...

FLINCH

Alex PEATTIE + TAYLOR

WILL YOU PLEASE JUST DO WHAT YOU'RE TOLD..

LOOK, THIS IS THE FIRST TIME I'VE HAD TO DO THE WASHING UP IN A RESTAURANT TO PAY FOR MY MEAL..

AND I'VE BEEN APPALLED TO LEARN THAT THE GOING RATE FOR A DISHWASHER IS £1·50 AN HOUR. I NEVER KNEW ANYONE COULD BE SO BADLY PAID...

SO WHAT?

IT PROBABLY MEANS NOTHING TO YOU BUT I'VE SPENT THREE HOURS WORKING ALONGSIDE THESE CHAPS, AND I'M VERY CONCERNED ABOUT THEM.

PLEASE, SIR. I'M BEGGING YOU. JUST GO HOME NOW.

ABSOLUTELY NOT. I'VE ONLY DONE £4·50'S WORTH. THEY'LL THINK I DINED ON OMELETTE AND CHIPS.

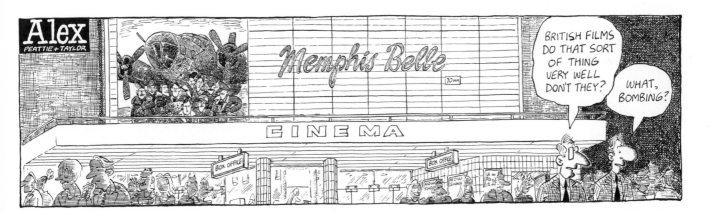

Alex PEATTIE + TAYLOR

SO WERE YOU WELL TREATED WHILE YOU WERE DETAINED IN KUWAIT CITY, GREG?

I SUPPOSE I CAN'T COMPLAIN.

AFTER ALL WE WERE BEING HELD AT THE FIVE STAR "IMPERIAL" HOTEL WITH ALL THE FACILITIES AT OUR DISPOSAL.

STILL, IT WAS A PRETTY UNPLEASANT EXPERIENCE BEING HELD IN A FIRST CLASS HOTEL UNDER THOSE CONDITIONS..

FOR FREE?

EXACTLY. NORMALLY I'D CLAIM FOR THE EXCELSIOR AND STAY WITH FRIENDS.

Alex PEATTIE + TAYLOR

ALTHOUGH WAR LOOKS INEVITABLE, THE MILITARY SEEM RESIGNED TO A LONG AND COSTLY STALEMATE.

WHICH INVOLVES THE PROSPECT OF BOREDOM AND FRUSTRATION SETTING IN HERE, AS WELL AS THE RISK OF WANING PUBLIC INTEREST BACK HOME.

OF COURSE THERE ARE OTHER STRATEGIES WHICH MUST MERIT CONSIDERATION.

WHAT, YOU MEAN THE OPTION OF SOMEONE GETTING INTO IRAQ AND TAKING OUT SADDAM HUSSEIN?

YES.

I EXPECT HE'D BE GUARDED ALL THE TIME THOUGH.

SURE, BUT IT'S WORTH A TRY...

...HE WOULDN'T BE THE FIRST PERSON TO BLURT OUT SOME GOOD COPY "OFF THE RECORD" AFTER A DECENT LUNCHEON...

ER... DOES ANYONE KNOW ANY GOOD RESTAURANTS IN BAGHDAD?

Alex
PEATTIE + TAYLOR

THESE DAYS PEOPLE IN THE CITY ARE TAKING A MUCH MORE RESPONSIBLE ATTITUDE. I MEAN, WITNESS THE CURRENT LEVEL OF CONCERN ABOUT THE ENVIRONMENT.

THERE WAS A TIME WHEN THE AVERAGE CITY SLICKER WOULDN'T GIVE A SECOND THOUGHT TO THE FUTURE AND LED A LIFE OF FRIVOLOUS SELF-INDULGENCE.

BUT NOW SUDDENLY PEOPLE HAVE FINALLY WOKEN UP TO THE DANGERS THAT THIS WORLD OF OURS IS FACING.

AN ECONOMIC RECESSION?

PRECISELY, AND THIS ECOLOGY FAD HAS QUITE RIGHTLY GONE STRAIGHT OUT OF THE WINDOW.

Alex
PEATTIE + TAYLOR

THE NEXT CANDIDATE: ALEX MASTERLEY. DIDN'T YOU KNOW HIM AT YOUR PREVIOUS BANK, RUPERT?

THAT'S RIGHT.

AS YOU KNOW, WHEN A CANDIDATE COMES IN FOR INTERVIEW HERE AT MEGABANK WE SUBJECT THEIR MOST RECENT SAMPLE OF HANDWRITING TO A GRAPHOLOGICAL ANALYSIS.

YES.

THE CLARITY AND LEGIBILITY OF THEIR SCRIPT IS INDICATIVE OF THEIR LEVEL OF CLEAR-HEADEDNESS.

AND THIS CHAP ALEX SCORED VERY WELL.

OH YES. GOOD SHOW.

IT'S AMAZING WHAT A CASUAL PERUSAL OF THIS SPECIMEN OF HANDWRITING REVEALS ABOUT THE PERSON WHO WROTE IT...

ABSOLUTELY NOTHING. IT'S THE MOST ILLEGIBLE VISITORS' BOOK ENTRY I'VE EVER SEEN.

YES. QUITE LAUDABLE CAUTION AGAINST HIS NAME AND THAT OF THE OUTPLACEMENT AGENCY BEING RECOGNISED.

Alex
PEATTIE + TAYLOR

IT'S HARD TO KNOW HOW TO START REBUILDING ONE'S PERSONAL SHARE PORTFOLIO IN THESE BEARISH TIMES OF BANKRUPTCIES AND REDUNDANCIES...

OH THERE ARE PLENTY OF BUSINESSES THAT FLOURISH IN A RECESSION, CLIVE. DEBT-RECOVERY COMPANIES, FOR EXAMPLE...

AND DON'T FORGET OUTPLACEMENT AGENCIES LIKE THE ONE WE'VE RECENTLY BENEFITED FROM. PERSONALLY I'VE INVESTED QUITE SUBSTANTIALLY IN THEIR STOCK. I'D ADVISE YOU TO DO THE SAME.

THANK GOODNESS YOU AND I ARE BACK IN SALARIED EMPLOYMENT AND IN A POSITION TO EXPLOIT THIS INVESTMENT OPPORTUNITY TO THE FULL...

BY SACKING A FEW PEOPLE.

COX, DICKSON AND MYERS ARE OUTSIDE AS YOU REQUESTED, ALEX.

Alex
PEATTIE + TAYLOR

THAT POOR CHAP MYERS - BEING SACKED BY YOU AS SOON AS HE GOT BACK FROM HIS HOLIDAY IN AUSTRALIA - IT CAME AS AN ABSOLUTE BOMBSHELL TO HIM.

HE STAGGERED OUT OF YOUR OFFICE COMPLETELY ASHEN-FACED AND JUST WANDERED AROUND THE OFFICE IN A DAZE. HE CLEARLY DIDN'T KNOW WHAT TIME OF DAY IT WAS.

HE THEN STUMBLED OUT SAYING HE WAS GOING HOME TO BED. DON'T YOU THINK THE MANNER AND TIMING OF YOUR ANNOUNCEMENT WAS A LITTLE THOUGHTLESS?

YES. YOU'RE RIGHT.

EVERYONE PROBABLY JUST ASSUMED HE HAD JET LAG. DAMN.

SNAP

Alex PEATTIE + TAYLOR

WHAT'S THIS, CLIVE? A MEMO TO RUPERT?

YES COMPLAINING ABOUT THE UNACCEPTABLE FLUORESCENT STRIP LIGHTING IN OUR OFFICE.

A LITTLE PRECIPITATE OF YOU SURELY?

NOT AT ALL. ONE'S GOT TO ACT ON SUCH MATTERS AS SOON AS ONE ARRIVES AT A NEW BANK.

IT'S WELL KNOWN WHAT PROBLEMS CAN BE CAUSED IF, IN ONE'S WORKING ENVIRONMENT, ONE IS CONSTANTLY UNDER THE HARSH GLARE OF THESE OVERHEAD STRIPLIGHTS.

YOU MEAN YOU'D HAVE TO CHANGE THAT FLATTERING SOFT-LIT STUDIO PHOTO OF YOURSELF ON YOUR OFFICE SECURITY PASS?

YES. IF I GOT CHALLENGED TO SHOW IT NO-ONE WOULD BELIEVE IT WAS ME.

Alex PEATTIE + TAYLOR

I SOMETIMES DESPAIR OF MY GOLF, ALEX.

NEVER SAY DIE, CLIVE.

AT THE MOMENT YOU TEND TO LOSE TO JUST ABOUT ALL COMERS. BUT REMEMBER GOLF IS A GAME WHERE EXPERIENCE COUNTS, RATHER THAN PHYSICAL FITNESS.

KEEP PLAYING LIKE THAT AND IN A FEW YEARS TIME YOU'LL BE A TOUGH OPPONENT. YOU'LL SHAME MEN FIFTEEN YEARS YOUR JUNIOR.

BECAUSE THEY'LL HAVE TO PLAY CHEEK-REDDENINGLY BADLY TO LET YOU BEAT THEM.

14TH TEE

Alex — PEATTIE + TAYLOR

So you're going to be on a charity ball committee?

That's right. Not uncommon these days, Clive.

I know. There are friends of mine whom I'd always assumed were just normal complacent selfish city types who've turned out to have been doing that sort of charity work in their spare time for years.

Yet none of them ever breathed a word about it to me. It was only when I found out about it by chance that I was able to appreciate what sort of people they really were...

Total stuck-up snobbish bastards. They didn't want to ask me to their balls.

One has to vet one's invitees very carefully.

Alex — PEATTIE + TAYLOR

So you're really sure about helping out with this charity ball?

YUP.

Do you have any idea of the kind of unforeseen arduous time-consuming practical tasks which a commitment like that entails?

Of course.

Alex, can you really see yourself rushing round to the hotel at the last minute with car-loads of raffle prizes, programmes, place settings and table decorations?

Have you thought seriously about what you'll have to go through?

ER...

Oh my god. The tradesman's entrance?

Exactly.

GULP.

Alex PEATTIE + TAYLOR

I DON'T WANT TO BE TOO CRITICAL OF ANYONE'S MOTIVATIONS... AFTER ALL IT IS £75 PER TICKET FOR THIS CHARITY BALL.

BUT IT DOES SEEM A SAD COMMENT ON PEOPLE'S MORAL FIBRE THAT ONE HAS TO ORGANISE AN EVENING LIKE THIS BEFORE THEY'LL PART WITH THEIR MONEY.

I SUPPOSE IT'S THE TIMES WE LIVE IN.

YES. IT'S RATHER A SHAME THAT PEOPLE NEED TO BE GIVEN EXCUSES TO DO WHAT WOULD ONCE HAVE BEEN CONSIDERED A NATURAL OBLIGATION.

WHAT, HAVE AN EVENING OF MINDLESS HEDONISM?

EXACTLY. WITHOUT JUSTIFYING IT BY DOING IT FOR CHARITY.

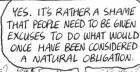
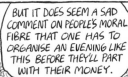

Alex PEATTIE + TAYLOR

OH DEAR. POOR OLD CLIVE. LOOK AT THAT.

OH IT'S ALL IN A GOOD CAUSE, PENNY.

IN THESE CHARITY AUCTIONS IT'S ALWAYS THE PEOPLE WHO'VE HAD MOST TO DRINK WHO ARE THE PEOPLE WHO END UP PAYING A LOT OF MONEY FOR THE ITEMS UNDER THE HAMMER.

WHICH EXPLAINS THE ALL TOO FORESEEABLE PREDICAMENT THAT CLIVE HAS ENDED UP IN.

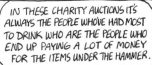

STILL SOBER.

YES. HE HASN'T MANAGED TO ATTRACT THE ATTENTION OF THE WINE WAITER OR THE AUCTIONEER ALL EVENING.

AHEM...

ANY MORE BIDS?

Alex PEATTIE + TAYLOR

OBVIOUSLY THIS BALL CAN'T POSSIBLY HOPE TO RAISE AS MUCH MONEY FOR CHARITY AS PREVIOUS YEARS' EVENTS HAVE DONE.

NO.

WITH THE ECONOMIC RECESSION AND THE NEW MOOD OF AUSTERITY INEVITABLY GUESTS CAN NO LONGER AFFORD THE LAVISH EXPENDITURE OF TIMES GONE BY.

IT'S SAD OF COURSE, BUT ONE DOES DETECT CERTAIN CHANGES.

YES, I'D NOTICED...

THE FOOD AND WINE ARE DEFINITELY OF A MUCH HIGHER STANDARD THAN LAST YEAR.

CLEARLY PEOPLE NEED TO FEEL THE TICKET PRICE REPRESENTS BETTER VALUE FOR MONEY THESE DAYS.

Alex PEATTIE + TAYLOR

FRANKLY, CLIVE, US CHARITY WORKERS GET SICK OF LISTENING TO CONDESCENDING EXPRESSIONS OF SYMPATHY FOR THE PEOPLE THESE EVENTS ARE ABOUT.

OH.

YOU'RE SO TYPICAL. YOU NEVER HAVE TO MEET THEM. IT'S EASY FOR YOU TO CLAIM YOU FEEL PITY FOR THEM AND SYMPATHISE WITH THE DREADFUL CONDITIONS THEY HAVE TO LIVE WITH.

BUT IT'S TRUE. I DO FEEL SORRY FOR THEM...

THAT'S A PATRONISING ATTITUDE WHICH IS TOTALLY INSINCERE. WHEN IT COMES TO THE CRUNCH YOUR SORT ALWAYS FAILS TO TRANSLATE WHAT YOU PROFESS INTO WHAT YOU ACTUALLY DO.

YES. I ADMIT IT. YOU'RE RIGHT...

...I'D PROBABLY CRINGE AND GROVEL AND UTTERLY LOSE MY DIGNITY...

QUITE. INTERFACING WITH ROYAL PERSONAGES TAKES PRACTICE.

Alex PEATTIE + TAYLOR

OBVIOUSLY WE WANT A TOP STOCKBROKING FIRM FOR THIS DEAL...

YES BUT BE WARY OF JUDGING BY A SINGLE CONVERSATION WITH AN INDIVIDUAL BROKER.

WELL, I CHATTED TO THIS CHAP EVERY AFTERNOON LAST WEEK. HE ALWAYS STRUCK ME AS CALM, CLEAR-HEADED, ATTENTIVE AND WELL-INFORMED ON THE MARKETS.

THAT SEEMS PRETTY CONCLUSIVE...

MAINTAIN DAILY CONTACT WITH HIM UNTIL THE END OF THE WEEK AND IF HE REMAINS CONSISTENT YOU'LL KNOW.

THAT THEY'RE IN DIRE FINANCIAL TROUBLE. IT SOUNDS LIKE THEY'VE HAD TO CANCEL THEIR CHRISTMAS LUNCH.

ER... OH.

Alex PEATTIE + TAYLOR

MEETING PEOPLE AT THESE CHRISTMAS PARTIES, IT'S NOTICEABLE HOW THE CARING 90s-TYPE VALUES HAVE FILTERED THROUGH TO THE CITY.

LIKE THE WAY PEOPLE ARE OPENING UP ABOUT THEIR PERSONAL LIVES, TAKING AN INTEREST IN BABIES ETC. AND PREPARED TO DISCUSS ISSUES AFFECTING SOCIETY AND THE PLANET AS A WHOLE.

TRULY AN AMAZING CONTRAST WHEN ONE THINKS WHAT SORT OF THINGS THEY USED TO BANG ON ABOUT BACK IN THE GREEDY GRASPING EIGHTIES.

DEALS THEY HAD DONE?

FAT CHANCE OF THAT THESE DAYS.

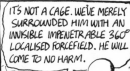

Alex PEATTIE + TAYLOR

MY GOD! YOU CALL YOURSELVES CIVILIZED? HOW COULD YOU INFLICT THAT KIND OF INDIGNITY ON CLIVE? CAGING HIM UP LIKE THAT?

CALM YOURSELF...

IT'S NOT A CAGE. WE'VE MERELY SURROUNDED HIM WITH AN INVISIBLE IMPENETRABLE 360° LOCALISED FORCEFIELD. HE WILL COME TO NO HARM.

HAVE YOU NO PITY?

CAN'T YOU SEE THE WAY HE'S DISPLAYED REDUCES HIM TO THE APPEARANCE OF THE LOWLIEST AND MOST WRETCHED STATE THAT EXISTS?

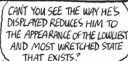

OR DON'T YOU HAVE STREET THEATRE MIME ARTISTS ON YOUR PLANET?

PAT
PAT

Alex PEATTIE + TAYLOR

MAY I HAVE A GO WITH THAT?

IF YOU ARE SURE YOU'RE FAMILIAR WITH SUCH A DEVICE.

WE CARRY THESE FOR OUR OWN PROTECTION. WE WOULD NEVER LEAVE OUR VESSEL WITHOUT ONE. THIS IS A DANGEROUS AND POSSIBLY HOSTILE WORLD.

OF COURSE.

PLEASE BE VERY CAREFUL WHERE YOU POINT IT.

DON'T WORRY I KNOW THAT...

THERE...

ZAP!

YOU STUPID STUPID MORON.

I THOUGHT IT WAS GOING TO LOCK THE DOORS.

Alex PEATTIE + TAYLOR

AS A GENERAL MEASURE DURING THE GULF CRISIS WE AMERICANS HAVE BEEN ADVISED NOT TO DRAW ATTENTION TO OURSELVES IN PUBLIC.

OUR BANK HELD A TOP LEVEL MEETING TO DISCUSS THE MATTER OF PROTECTING ITS EMPLOYEES AND HAS CIRCULATED AN INTERNAL MEMO OF ITS PROPOSALS.

THOUGH IN VIEW OF THE NATURE OF SUCH RESOLUTIONS IT WOULD NOT BE ADVISABLE FOR ME TO SAY EXACTLY WHAT THE BANK HAS DECIDED TO DO ABOUT OUR SAFETY.

I KNOW...

"PRIORITIZE" IT.

SHHH. JEEZ, CLIVE KEEP YOUR VOICE DOWN.

Alex PEATTIE + TAYLOR

I HEAR CLIFFORD'S PULLED OUT OF ALL HIS INTERNATIONAL MEETINGS...

THAT'S RIGHT. HE WON'T FLY ANYWHERE.

LIKE SO MANY BUSINESS TRAVELLERS, HE'S FEARFUL OF A TERRORIST MASQUERADING AS A PASSENGER AND SLIPPING A SUITCASE BOMB IN THE HOLD.

GOOD LORD. CLIFFORD? I'M AMAZED.

QUITE SO. IT MAY BE UNFASHIONABLE IN THESE SO-CALLED "CARING 90'S", BUT I FEEL THIS WAR SHOULD BE GIVING A CAPTAIN OF INDUSTRY AN OCCASION TO MAKE A PUBLIC DISPLAY OF THE ATTRIBUTES ONE WOULD EXPECT HIM TO POSSESS.

EXACTLY.

...LIKE A PRIVATE JET.

ONE CAN ONLY CONCLUDE HE DOESN'T HAVE ONE.

Alex PEATTIE + TAYLOR

IT REALLY IS A PRIVILEGE TO WORK WITH AN EXPERIENCED MIDDLE EAST CORRESPONDENT LIKE GREG MASTERLEY.

HE EPITOMISES EVERYTHING ABOUT THE PROFESSION. HE'S AN INSPIRATION TO US ALL.

YOU KNOW, WHEN THE AIR-RAID SIRENS GO OFF WARNING OF INCOMING MISSILES MOST OF THE JOURNALISTS JUST HEAD STRAIGHT FOR THE NEAREST BUNKER - BUT NOT GREG...

NO, HE'LL ALWAYS OFFER TO TAKE YOU TO A MUCH NICER ONE HE KNOWS ACROSS ON THE OTHER SIDE OF TOWN.

Alex PEATTIE + TAYLOR

THE INITIAL STAGES OF THIS WAR HAVE BEEN QUITE UNPRECEDENTED, WITH ITS PRECISION BOMBING AND ANTI-MISSILE MISSILES.

IT HAS PRODUCED THE REMARKABLE PHENOMENON OF CORRESPONDENTS LIKE US SITTING IN OUR HOTEL ROOMS AND OBSERVING IT ALL HAPPENING AROUND US.

OF COURSE PRETTY SOON THE FOCUS OF THE WAR WILL SHIFT TO A FRONT-LINE INFANTRY ASSAULT AND WE WILL SEE A REVERSION TO MORE TRADITIONAL JOURNALISTIC PRACTICE...

SITTING IN OUR HOTEL ROOMS AND MAKING IT ALL UP?

EXACTLY.

Alex PEATTIE + TAYLOR

THESE CRASH BARRIERS OUTSIDE YOUR FRONT ENTRANCE ARE NEW

JUST HAD THEM PUT UP.

BROOKLYN BANK

BEING AN AMERICAN BANK WE HAVE TO TAKE THE APPROPRIATE MEASURES IN THE PRESENT INTERNATIONAL CRISIS.

BETTER SAFE THAN SORRY I SUPPOSE.

RIGHT. YOU NEVER KNOW WHEN SOME FANATIC AT THE WHEEL OF A CAR WILL TRY TO PERPETRATE SOME DESPERATE ACTION IN A BID FOR THE IMMORTALITY ACHIEVED BY LEGENDARY FIGURES OF THE PAST.

SUCH AS THE APOCRYPHAL SACKED TRADER WHO DROVE HIS PORSCHE INTO HIS BANK'S ENTRANCE, SET OFF HIS CAR ALARM AND DROPPED HIS KEYS DOWN A DRAIN?

CORRECT. AND I'M IMPLEMENTING THE NEXT ROUND OF REDUNDANCIES NOW.

Alex PEATTIE + TAYLOR

HIGGINS FROM THE "GLOBE" IS IN THERE WITH HIM NOW.

CAPT. HAWKINS PRESS LIAISON OFFICER

HEY! I CAN'T BELIEVE IT. YOU'RE GOING THROUGH MY TEXT CHANGING AND DELETING PHRASES AND ADJECTIVES.

LOOK. THIS IS STANDARD PROCEDURE.

SCRIBBLE

WELL I DON'T THINK IT'S FAIR. WHY SHOULD I DO ALL THAT WORK JUST TO HAVE YOU DO THIS TO IT?

WAKE UP. THIS IS THE REAL WORLD SONNY.

IF YOU'RE QUITE FINISHED SUBTLY ALTERING EVERYTHING I'VE WRITTEN...

YES I THINK THIS IS FIT TO BE PRINTED NOW..

I'LL JUST ADD MY NAME AT THE BOTTOM AND IF I COULD BORROW YOUR FAX MACHINE I'LL SEND IT STRAIGHT OFF TO MY EDITOR.

BLOODY JOURNALISTS. THAT'S THE LAST PRESS RELEASE YOU GET FROM ME.

Alex
PEATTIE + TAYLOR

PRESCOTT & MAITLAND OUTPLACEMENT AGENCY.

I JUST SAW ONE OF OUR EX-CLIENTS IN THE STREET: A CHAP CALLED CLIVE, REMEMBER HIM?

OH YES. WE COUNSELLED HIM AFTER HE WAS MADE REDUNDANT LAST SUMMER.

YOU KNOW, A PERIOD OF UNEMPLOYMENT IS THE MOST HURTFUL AND SHAMING THING AN EXECUTIVE CAN UNDERGO. I WORKED CLOSELY WITH CLIVE OVER THE WEEKS HELPING HIM BUILD BACK HIS SELF-ESTEEM AND A POSITIVE ATTITUDE.

YET WHEN I ENCOUNTERED HIM IN THE STREET I WONDERED WHAT THE POINT OF IT ALL HAD BEEN. IT WAS AS IF HE'D FORGOTTEN EVERYTHING WE'D BEEN THROUGH TOGETHER.

HE SAID HELLO AND CHATTED AMIABLY TO ME FOR 5 MINUTES.

WHAT INSTEAD OF WALKING PAST PRETENDING NEVER TO HAVE SEEN YOU BEFORE? HOW DEMORALISING.

Alex
PEATTIE + TAYLOR

IN COMPARISON TO THE YUPPIE 80s, I THINK 90s DINNER PARTIES SHOW HOW MUCH LESS CONCERNED WE ARE ABOUT FORM.

SIGH. YES.

WE SIMPLY DON'T GIVE A DAMN ABOUT APPEARING DYNAMIC THESE DAYS. WE JUST ENJOY FLOPPING DOWN AFTER DINNER, INDULGING IN IDLE CONVERSATION

THAT'S RIGHT.

IN THE BOOM YEARS WE WERE MUCH TOO UPTIGHT TO ALLOW OURSELVES TO BE SEEN RELAXING IN THE COMFORT OF EASY CHAIRS LIKE THIS..

WE'D BOTH BE PRETENDING TO HAVE FALLEN ASLEEP IN THEM THROUGH OVERWORK.

WELL, NO ONE WOULD BELIEVE IT NOWADAYS ANYWAY.

Alex
PEATTIE + TAYLOR

WELL, PENNY, I'M NOT LOOKING FORWARD TO SPENDING AN EVENING LISTENING TO YOUR TRENDY FRIENDS BEMOANING THE NEWS FROM THE GULF.

NOW THAT JOURNALISTS HAVE STARTED SENDING BACK THE FIRST T.V. PICTURES FROM POST-WAR KUWAIT I'M AFRAID A BACKLASH FROM CERTAIN PEOPLE IS INEVITABLE.

AND IT'S ALWAYS THE ARTY AND LIBERAL-INTELLECTUAL TYPES WHO INDULGE IN SUCH POINTLESS HAND-WRINGING AND WISE-AFTER-THE-EVENT REGRETS...

OH DEAR. I THINK THE AMATEUR VIDEOS SHOT DURING THE OCCUPATION WERE MUCH MORE SPONTANEOUS...

YES. THERE'S A REALLY NICE GRAINY QUALITY YOU GET WITH A CAMCORDER...

TOLD YOU.

Alex
PEATTIE + TAYLOR

VERY POOR TURN-OUT THIS YEAR.

TRUE, CLIVE. BUT IN MANY RESPECTS I'M PLEASED THAT BANKING IS NO LONGER SUCH A FASHIONABLE CAREER OPTION.

MEGABANK GRADUATE RECRUITMENT PARTY

AS A HOST IT WAS ALWAYS HARD TO CREATE THE RIGHT IMPRESSION IN THE CRUSH OF PREVIOUS YEARS. ONE ALWAYS APPEARED TO BE TOO BUSY TO TALK TO ANY INDIVIDUAL GRADUATE FOR A LONG TIME.

WHEREAS THE MORE UNDERPOPULATED FEEL OF TODAY'S EVENT PERMITS ONE TO ENJOY A MORE SATISFACTORY DEGREE OF SOCIAL INTERACTION.

LIKE POINTEDLY SNUBBING SOMEONE?

YES. WHEN I TOLD HIM I HAD TO GO AND CIRCULATE I THINK HE GOT THE MESSAGE.

Alex
PEATTIE + TAYLOR

MEN'S THERAPY GROUP.

SORRY I'M LATE.

OH DEAR. LATENESS IMPLIES RELUCTANCE, BRIAN.

DON'T WORRY. I KNOW HIS TYPE. THINK OF TIM WHEN HE STARTED. VERY RELUCTANT HE WAS THEN TOO.

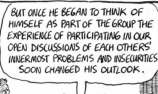

BUT ONCE HE BEGAN TO THINK OF HIMSELF AS PART OF THE GROUP THE EXPERIENCE OF PARTICIPATING IN OUR OPEN DISCUSSIONS OF EACH OTHERS' INNERMOST PROBLEMS AND INSECURITIES SOON CHANGED HIS OUTLOOK.

THAT'S TRUE.

JUST LOOK AT HIM NOW. HE'S HERE EVERY WEEK, ON TIME AND HE'S NEVER TRIED TO LEAVE EARLY. HE SAYS HE WOULDN'T WANT TO MISS A SINGLE MINUTE.

RIGHT.

TOTALLY PARANOID ISN'T HE?

-THAT EVERYONE WOULD TALK ABOUT HIM BEHIND HIS BACK. YES.

Alex
PEATTIE + TAYLOR

CLIVE. THIS MUTUAL HAND-MASSAGING EXERCISE IS VERY IMPORTANT TO BREAK DOWN THE BARRIERS THAT FREQUENTLY EXIST IN MALE RELATIONSHIPS.

THE WAY YOU RECOILED IN EMBARRASSMENT WHEN RAY TOOK YOUR HAND VISIBLY DEMONSTRATED ALL YOUR INHERENT HANG-UPS ABOUT THIS SITUATION.

I'M SORRY...

IT'S NOT THAT I'M PREJUDICED OR ANYTHING, BUT WHEN A MAN I'VE NEVER MET BEFORE FONDLES MY HAND IN THAT INTIMATE WAY I SUPPOSE I ALWAYS HAVE A FEAR HE MIGHT BE A YOU-KNOW-WHAT...

A MASON? HERE?

WELL, YOU'VE GOT TO BE ON YOUR GUARD.

Alex
PEATTIE + TAYLOR

AS IT'S THE BREAK CAN I GET EVERYONE SOME COFFEE?

CLIVE, IN THIS GROUP WE DON'T PERMIT SUCH ROLE-PLAYING. PEOPLE GET THEIR OWN COFFEE.

YOUR OFFER IS MERELY YOUR WAY OF CONFORMING TO THE POLITE DEFERENTIAL NORMS OF GROUP SOCIAL BEHAVIOUR. IT'S AN EXPRESSION OF YOUR REPRESSION AND GUILT.

OH, I SEE.

WE'RE TRYING TO ENCOURAGE EVERYONE HERE TO EXPRESS THEIR FRUSTRATIONS AND LATENT ANGER BY SCREAMING AND MAKING PHYSICAL CONTACT.

RIGHT.

SO YOU MEAN YOU HAVE AN AUTOMATIC COFFEE VENDING MACHINE?

Alex
PEATTIE + TAYLOR

AS MEN, I THINK WE ALL HAVE TO ADMIT TO OURSELVES THE SEXUAL ASSOCIATIONS EVOKED BY RECENT WAR PICTURES FROM THE GULF.

NOD.

FOR EXAMPLE THE ACTUAL LONG SMOOTH STREAMLINED SHAPE OF THE CRUISE MISSILE IS PRIMARILY A MALE ORIENTED IMAGE.

YES.

INDEED.

AND THE CONNOTATION OF GUIDING THESE WEAPONS TOWARDS INDIVIDUAL TARGET BUILDINGS IS OBVIOUS.

YES. YES, YES. MMM

OH YES.

AND AS FOR THE DISTURBING RAMIFICATIONS OF THEM ACTUALLY PENETRATING THROUGH A NARROW AIR VENT OR DOORWAY...

YEAH

YES. NOT TO MENTION EXPLODING IMMEDIATELY.

BEG PARDON?

*@$%!

Alex PEATTIE + TAYLOR

I'VE ALWAYS HATED THE FACT THAT IN THE CLASSIC SOCIAL SITUATIONS WHEN MALES GET TOGETHER THERE'S SUCH A TABOO AGAINST THE SHEDDING OF TEARS.

THE MOCKERY AND CONTEMPT WHICH IS HEAPED UPON YOU IF YOU SHOW ANY SIGNS OF WEAKNESS OR VULNERABILITY IN PUBLIC MAKES ONE SO INHIBITED.

IT'S SO DIFFERENT WHEN I'M IN THE COMPANY OF MY THERAPY GROUP. ON THOSE OCCASIONS WHERE THE TEARS WELL UP YOU ARE GREETED WITH KIND SYMPATHY AND UNDER-STANDING. IT REALLY IS MY UTTER FANTASY.

I KNOW HOW YOU FEEL, CLIVE. MY LAMB KORMA IS VICIOUS AS WELL.

ANOTHER JUG OF WATER PLEASE, WAITER.

I'M NOT GOING TO FINISH MINE.

TAJ MAHAL

Alex PEATTIE + TAYLOR

LOOK. ALL I'M SAYING IS COULD YOU TRY TO BE MORE QUIET?

OKAY, CLIVE YOU CAN STOP NOW.

FINE. NOW WE'VE EACH STARTED BY ROLE PLAYING THE CLASSIC CONFRONTATION SCENARIO OF HAVING A SHOWDOWN WITH A NOISY NEIGHBOUR.

IN THE CONTEXT OF THESE THERAPY GROUPS IT'S VITAL TO GAIN BASIC CONFIDENCE TO HANDLE SUCH SITUATIONS ASSERTIVELY.

ANY ONE OF US FROM TIME TO TIME MAY BE CALLED UPON TO USE SUCH SKILLS OUTSIDE THE CLASS.

ER... THE CHAPS AND I WONDERED IF YOU'D MIND ER KEEPING IT DOWN A BIT...

MEN'S THERAPY GROUP

PRIMAL SCREAM GROUP

Alex PEATTIE + TAYLOR

MEN'S THERAPY GROUP

GOSH.

LOOK AT TIM. HE WAS ALWAYS THE MOST PARANOID AND UPTIGHT PERSON IN THE MEN'S GROUP.

IT'S AMAZING TO SEE HOW LIFTING THE TABOOS AGAINST TOUCHING ONE ANOTHER HAS FREED HIS BEHAVIOUR FROM INHIBITION. WE'LL SOON HAVE HIM TALKING OPENLY ABOUT HIS PROBLEMS.

SQUEEZE

HE SEEMS SO MUCH MORE RELAXED.

YES. SINCE BEING ALLOWED TO MAKE PHYSICAL CONTACT WITH THE OTHER GROUP MEMBERS HE'S ABLE TO GIVE VENT TO THE BASIC YEARNINGS HE'S BEEN HAVING TO REPRESS ALL THIS TIME...

CUFF

IE: FRISKING EVERYONE ELSE FOR CONCEALED WIRES OR RECORDING EQUIPMENT.

EEK!

Alex PEATTIE + TAYLOR

NUDGE

OOPS. SORRY, ROBERT.

AHAH!

NOW, CLIVE, THE WAY YOU REACTED TO ACCIDENTAL PHYSICAL CONTACT IS A PERFECT ILLUSTRATION OF HOW WE BRITISH ARE HUNG UP ABOUT TOUCH.

...THE BRIEF EMBARRASSED MURMER OF APOLOGY, EYES AVERTED... BOTH PARTIES PRETENDING IT DIDN'T HAPPEN... I MEAN: HOW REPRESSED!

IT'S NOT NATURAL TO ALWAYS BE SO EMOTIONALLY CONSTRAINED, CLIVE. YOU OUGHT TO TRY TO TUNE IN TO YOUR INSTINCTS... LET YOURSELF GO A LITTLE... STOP BOTTLING EVERYTHING UP.

RIGHT.

I'M SORRY... I REALLY DO FEEL SO WRETCHED ABOUT INVADING YOUR BODY SPACE... I KNOW I'M JUST AN UTTER NOTHING AND YOU MUST BE FURIOUS WITH ME...

Alex PEATTIE + TAYLOR

RELAX, CLIVE. THE IDEA OF THIS "CAR WASH" EXERCISE IS TO ACCUSTOM YOU TO BEING TOUCHED BY THE OTHERS AS YOU WALK BETWEEN THEM.

ERK.

ANYONE WHO'S EVER TRAVELLED IN ASIA WILL KNOW THAT BRITISH OVER-SENSITIVITY TO PHYSICAL CONTACT SEEMS ABSURD TO PEOPLE FROM EASTERN CULTURES.

EEK.

SO JUST CLOSE YOUR EYES AND IMAGINE YOURSELF TO BE ONE OF THEM. EXPERIENCE THE TOUCHES OF OTHERS WITHOUT FEELING THE USUAL WESTERN HANG-UPS AND GUILT.

RIGHT...

OH GET AWAY FROM ME YOU HORRIBLE URCHINS YOU WON'T GET A SINGLE RUPEE OUT OF ME.

Alex PEATTIE + TAYLOR

CLIVE'S REALLY GETTING INTO THIS SUBSTITUTION THERAPY.

WHY DO YOU NEVER PAY ANY ATTENTION TO ME?

SHOUTING AT AN INANIMATE OBJECT - IN THIS CASE A CUSHION - HELPS HIM DEAL WITH SITUATIONS OF DEEPLY INBRED PSYCHOLOGICAL FRUSTRATION.

FOR ONCE WILL YOU JUST LISTEN TO ME AND SHUT UP!

THIS EXERCISE SHOULD HELP HIM LEARN TO COPE WITH SIMILAR CONFRONTATION SITUATIONS WHEN THEY OCCUR IN REAL LIFE.

YOU ALWAYS IGNORE ME. NOW FOR ONCE I WANT YOU TO DO WHAT I SAY AND BE QUIET!

SHUT UP! SHUT UP! WHY DO YOU NEVER PAY ANY ATTENTION TO ME?

BEEEEEEEP.

CLIVE, WHY DON'T YOU JUST GET RID OF THAT VOICE RESPONSE ALARM CLOCK?

Alex — PEATTIE + TAYLOR

WELL CLIVE THAT'S THE LAST TIME YOU'LL BE ASKED TO ATTEND A WEEKEND CONFERENCE AT LORD NORRINGTON'S COUNTRY ESTATE. YOU WERE AN EMBARRASSMENT

OH YES... I WANTED TO APOLOGISE FOR THAT...

YOU SIMPLY MUST LEARN THE DIFFERENCE BETWEEN CASUAL AND INFORMAL ATTIRE, CLIVE. PATTERNED SOCKS MAY BE PERMISSIBLE AT SUCH OCCASIONS BUT AS A CITY MAN IT IS DE RIGUEUR TO BE WEARING A SUIT.

I KNOW... I'M SORRY.

YOU STUCK OUT LIKE A SORE THUMB WHEN YOU TURNED UP IN THAT SCRUFFY HACKING JACKET AND BAGGY OLD TROUSERS. HAVE YOU ANY IDEA WHAT YOU LOOKED LIKE?

ER... YES...

... LIKE A LORD.

EXACTLY. YOU COMPLETELY UPSTAGED NORRINGTON IN THE GROUP PHOTO.

Alex — PEATTIE + TAYLOR

I SEE YOUR JOURNALIST FRIEND ANGUS HUGHES OF THE ECHO HAS RETIRED.

YOU'RE JOKING! WHEN? I WISH HE'D TOLD ME...

I'VE BEEN ONE OF THE MOST TRUSTED AND CLOSEST OF HIS CITY CONTACTS FOR YEARS... OUR LUNCHTIME GOSSIP SESSIONS HAVE BECOME SOMETHING OF AN INSTITUTION.

AND I NEED HARDLY SAY HOW VALUABLE IT'S BEEN FOR SOMEONE LIKE MYSELF TO HAVE A CHANNEL FOR GETTING CERTAIN STORIES INTO PRINT.

INDEED.

AND NOW HE JUST QUIETLY QUITS HIS JOB WITHOUT EVEN ALLOWING ME A CHANCE TO GIVE HIM THE SEND-OFF I'D ALWAYS PLANNED.

A PACK OF COMPLETE LIES PLANTED IN HIS COLUMN BY ME...DAMN.

WELL I SUPPOSE HE GUESSED WHAT WOULD HAPPEN ONCE HE STOPPED BEING WORTH CULTIVATING.

Alex
PEATTIE+TAYLOR

...AND IN MY DREAM IT'S MY UNIVERSITY FINALS... I OPEN UP MY EXAM PAPER AND I REALISE I CAN'T UNDERSTAND A SINGLE QUESTION. I'M TOTALLY UNPREPARED... WHAT DOES IT MEAN?

IT WAS YOUR SUBCONSCIOUS MIND CREATING A SIMPLE IMAGE OF FAILURE AND INADEQUACY TO ALLEVIATE A SENSE OF SHAME AND SELF-REPROACH YOU'VE BEEN UNABLE TO ACKNOWLEDGE OPENLY, CLIVE.

OH.

IN YOUR DREAM ONE SEES THE CLASSIC SUBLIMATION OF THE GUILT YOU FEEL ABOUT THE EXPECTATIONS OTHERS HAVE OF YOU... IN FACT ALMOST ALL STUDENTS HAVE EXPERIENCE OF THE SAME THING.

REALLY?

WHAT, CLAIMING NOT TO HAVE DONE ANY REVISION WHEN THEY'VE BEEN SNEAKILY SWOTTING IN SECRET?

YES. I BET YOU GOT A FIRST DIDN'T YOU?

Alex
PEATTIE+TAYLOR

YOU KNOW I WAS TELLING YOU LAST WEEK THAT I WAS CONVINCED THAT EVERYONE AT WORK WAS PLOTTING AND TALKING ABOUT ME BEHIND MY BACK?

YES.

AND I THOUGHT PEOPLE STOPPED TALKING WHEN I CAME INTO A ROOM AND STARTED LAUGHING WHEN I WENT OUT AGAIN?

YES. WAS THERE MORE?

WELL ON FRIDAY I WAS OBSESSED WITH THE IDEA THAT I WAS BEING FOLLOWED AND THAT THERE WERE PEOPLE HIDING IN THE EMPTY ROOMS WAITING FOR ME WHEN I GOT IN FROM WORK.

BUT THERE WEREN'T? YOU NOW REALISE IT WAS ALL A DELUSION AND A FANTASY?

YES.

AND IN FACT NO-ONE WAS ORGANISING A SURPRISE BIRTHDAY PARTY FOR YOU?

NO. THE BASTARDS. THEY'D COMPLETELY FORGOTTEN.

Alex
PEATTIE + TAYLOR

ANYWAY, I'M TRAVELLING ON A TRAIN AND LOOKING ON HELPLESSLY AS THE MOUTH OF A SINISTER BLACK TUNNEL LOOMS CLOSER AND CLOSER...

I SEE...

...THEN JUST AS THE LOCOMOTIVE GOES IN I WAKE UP IN A COLD SWEAT FILLED WITH A SENSE OF DREAD AND FOREBODING.

HMMM...WELL I'M SURE YOU DON'T NEED A FREUDIAN ANALYST TO TELL YOU WHAT KIND OF ANXIETY IS SUGGESTED BY YOUR DREAMS OF A TRAIN ENTERING A TUNNEL...

NO. AM I EVER GOING TO BE OKAY?

LOOK, CLIVE, I'M AFRAID IT MAY TAKE TIME AND A LOT OF WORK WILL HAVE TO BE DONE BEFORE YOU CAN BE FREE OF THIS FEAR.

BUT ONE DAY? IS THERE HOPE?

YES. YES. I'M SURE EVENTUALLY YOU'LL BE ABLE TO OBTAIN PORTABLE TELEPHONES WHICH WORK UNDERGROUND.

PHEW.

Alex
PEATTIE + TAYLOR

AT FIRST I DIDN'T KNOW WHAT TO THINK THE DAY BRIDGET TOLD ME SHE WAS PREGNANT. IT TOOK ME TOTALLY BY SURPRISE.

IT WASN'T UNTIL SHE GOT OUT HER DIARY AND WE STARTED TALKING DATES THAT THE REALITY OF THE SITUATION REALLY SANK IN. I DIDN'T KNOW WHETHER TO LAUGH OR CRY.

I SHOULD HAVE NOTICED EARLIER BUT I'M JUST NOT VERY OBSERVANT. AFTER ALL, SHE'S REGULAR AS CLOCKWORK. IN THE FOUR YEARS WE'VE LIVED TOGETHER SHE'S NEVER MISSED A SINGLE ONE.

AN APRIL FOOLS?

YES. TALK ABOUT BEING TAKEN FOR A SUCKER.

SHE HAD A GOLDEN PARACHUTE.

MARY POPPINS

Alex
PEATTIE + TAYLOR

I SAY. WHAT A DEVASTATINGLY ATTRACTIVE WOMAN.

YOW!

SLAP CLENCH

HONESTLY, CLIVE. THERE WAS NO CALL FOR YOU TO INDULGE IN THAT MINDLESS FLEXED-FOREARM, CLENCHED-FIST GESTICULATION.

ER... OH... SORRY, ALEX IT'S A CONDITIONED REFLEX.

I KNOW IT'S STUPID BUT THERE'S SOMETHING ABOUT OUR PREDOMINANTLY MALE OFFICE ENVIRONMENT WHICH SEEMS TO TRIGGER A NEED IN ME TO MAKE SILLY MACHO GESTURES...

LIKE GIVING BLOOD REGULARLY... OUCH OUCH OUCH...

YOU CAN'T GO ON FLINCHING LIKE THAT WHENEVER YOU SEE A NURSE, CLIVE. IT'S PATHETIC.

RUB RUB

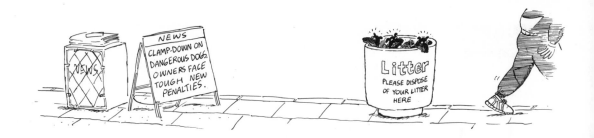

Alex PEATTIE + TAYLOR

URGH... LOOK WHAT IT IS OVER THERE, BARKING ALL OVER THE PLACE. THOSE PIT-BULL BREEDERS HAVE A LOT TO ANSWER FOR... HORRIBLE CREATURES, WRECKING THE NEIGHBOURHOOD...WORSE THAN TOSAS, IF YOU ASK ME... THEY SHOULD NEVER HAVE BEEN ALLOWED TO PROLIFERATE IN THIS MANNER.

IT'S ONLY A PUPPY.

WOOF WOOF

URGH... LOOK WHAT IT IS OVER THERE, PARKING ALL OVER THE PLACE. THOSE PITIFUL BLEEDERS HAVE A LOT TO ANSWER FOR... HORRIBLE CREATURES, WRECKING THE NEIGHBOURHOOD...WORSE THAN TOSSERS, IF YOU ASK ME... THEY SHOULD NEVER HAVE BEEN ALLOWED TO PROLIFERATE IN THIS MANOR.

IT'S ONLY A YUPPY.

Alex PEATTIE + TAYLOR

"MY GOD, CLIVE. WHERE DO YOU GET YOUR IDEAS FROM?"

ER WELL ER...

I WOULD HAVE THOUGHT THAT AT THE OCCASION OF A BALL TO RAISE MONEY FOR AFRICA THE ISSUE OF SOCIAL SEGREGATION OF BLACK AND WHITE IS HARDLY A MATTER WHICH CAN BE TAKEN LIGHTLY.

I ONLY ER...

AND DISPLAYING SUCH OUTMODED ATTITUDES BASED ON COMPLACENT ASSUMPTIONS ABOUT MASTER-SERVANT RELATIONSHIPS IS TOTALLY INSENSITIVE.

LOOK DON'T GET ME WRONG..

WHAT MAY BE SECOND NATURE TO SOME GENTLEMAN IN AN EX-COLONIAL TROPICAL OUTPOST IS NOT COMPATIBLE WITH THE SOCIAL STANDARDS OF MODERN-DAY BRITAIN.

SO GET RID OF THAT WHITE TUXEDO. OR PEOPLE WILL THINK YOU'RE A WAITER.

HUMPHREY BOGART ALWAYS WORE ONE...

Alex PEATTIE + TAYLOR

BARROW'S BREWERY

I'M SORRY, BUT WE'RE GOING TO HAVE TO MOVE THE SPONSOR'S ADVERTISING HOARDING.

BUT THE PHOTOGRAPHERS FROM THE LOCAL PAPERS ARE JUST LINING UP THEIR SHOTS...

YES, I KNOW THE IDEA WAS TO HAVE OUR CELEBRITY PHOTOGRAPHED WITH THAT LOGO BEHIND HIM TO GIVE THE SPONSOR'S NAME A DOLLOP OF FREE PROMOTION IN RETURN FOR THE DRINKS THEY PROVIDED...

BARROW'S BREWERY

BUT THE PHOTOGRAPHER FROM "THE INDEPENDENT" HAS JUST ARRIVED AND HE'S BOUND TO VIEW SUCH A SET-UP AS A CRASS ATTEMPT TO MANIPULATE PUBLICITY.

BARROW'S BREWERY

OH DEAR.. YOU'RE RIGHT. WE'D BETTER MOVE THE HOARDING.

LOVELY.... MMM... YES...

CLICK CLICK

BARROW'S BREWERY

ARTY TYPE, SEE?

RIGHT.

Alex
PEATTIE + TAYLOR

SORRY, CRESSIDA.

IT'S ALRIGHT. YOU CAN TURN THE MUSIC BACK UP. THERE'S NOTHING AMISS.

IT'S JUST THAT I THOUGHT I HEARD A SOUND FROM THE BABY ALARM AND AS YOU'RE SUPPOSED TO BE BABYSITTING FOR ALEX AND PENNY...

RELAX. EVERYTHING'S FINE... LISTEN...

AFTER ALL, THAT'S WHAT THOSE GADGETS ARE FOR. TO WARN YOU... FUNNY, I WAS SURE I HEARD A VOICE CALLING OUT... IT SOUNDED JUST LIKE WHAT YOU GET USED TO LISTENING OUT FOR.

...A TAXI'S RADIO PICKED UP BY THE BABY ALARM INDICATING THAT THE PARENTS' CAB HAS JUST PULLED UP OUTSIDE.

NO, IT'S JUST THE BABY CRYING. LET'S HAVE ANOTHER DRINK.

WAAAH... WAAH...

Alex
PEATTIE + TAYLOR

...THEY MUST UTTERLY DESPISE ME...

WHAT ARE YOU BLETHERING ON ABOUT, ALEX?

LOOK, CLIVE, AS YOU KNOW, ALL THE MUSICIANS AND ENTERTAINERS GAVE THEIR SERVICES FREE TONIGHT. BUT THERE WAS AN EXCEPTION... THE DISC JOCKEY. I HAD TO PAY HIM A SMALL FEE.

HE'D HAD TO CANCEL A PREVIOUS ENGAGEMENT, YOU SEE. I KNEW IT COULD BE MISINTERPRETED IF WORD GOT OUT... AND NOW THE PEOPLE I MOST WANTED IT KEPT SECRET FROM HAVE FOUND OUT.

THE MUSICIANS?

NO, STUFF THE MUSICIANS. I'M TALKING ABOUT THE GUESTS. THERE'S A RUMOUR GOING ROUND THAT I'VE HAD TO HIRE MY D.J.

OOH-ER.